# BOY OF OLD VIRGINIA
# ROBERT E. LEE

# Boy of Old Virginia
# ROBERT E. LEE

*by*
### HELEN A. MONSELL

Author of
*The Secret of the Chestnut Tree*

✱

*Illustrated by*
### CLOTILDE EMBREE FUNK

## THE BOBBS-MERRILL COMPANY
*Publishers*
INDIANAPOLIS                    NEW YORK

Printed in the United States of America

# TABLE OF CONTENTS

# FULL-PAGE ILLUSTRATIONS

# BOY OF OLD VIRGINIA
# ROBERT E. LEE

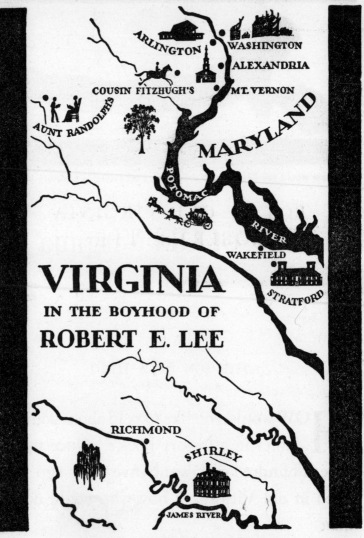

Virginia in the Boyhood of Robert E. Lee

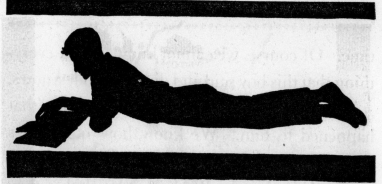

"How would you like to read about your own father in a history book?"

# Boy of Old Virginia

## I

### THE SON OF A HERO

HOW would you like to read about your own father in a history book? Once upon a time, a hundred and twenty-five years ago, there lived in old Virginia a boy who could do just that.

A hundred and twenty-five years ago is a long

time. Of course, we cannot know, today, everything that this boy said and did. Nobody knows.

We do know, though, many of the things that happened to him. We know how other boys and girls lived in those days. We know the games they played. We know the clothes they wore. All of these things I have put into one story.

The name of this boy's father was Henry Lee. He had been a hero in the Revolution. He had been Governor of Virginia. His soldiers had a nickname for him. They called him "Light-Horse Harry."

The boy's name was Robert Edward Lee. He was very proud of his father. He liked to be called Light-Horse Harry's son.

He tried always to be brave, as his father was brave. He loved Virginia as his father loved it. And the time came when the people of Virginia loved him even more than they had loved his father.   His name, too, was in every history book.

But it was not only in Virginia that people loved him.   All over the South, and all over the world, they loved him because he was brave, and unselfish, and because he tried always to do what he thought was right.

Today, if you ask anyone, "Who are the two greatest men ever born in Virginia?" the answer will be,

"George Washington and Robert E. Lee."

## II

### SAYING GOOD-BYE

WHEN Robert was a very little boy, he lived in a very big house, called Stratford. There were woods and fields all around the house. The Potomac River was not far away, blue in the sunlight. It was one of the prettiest places in all Virginia.

Stratford was a very big house. It was shaped like the letter "H." There were eight rooms on the first floor. There were eight rooms on the next floor. There were more rooms than Robert could count.

For Robert was a very little boy. He was the youngest of the Lee children. Brother Henry was a grown man. Carter was twelve years old. Ann was ten, and Smith was eight. But Robert was only three and a half.

Stratford

That was why he couldn't understand what was going on at Stratford one fine summer morning in 1810. He only knew that everything was a-hustle and a-bustle.

Mother and Mammy, his black nurse, were packing things in boxes and trunks. Father, at his desk, was tying letters and papers into packages.

Smith was hurrying around from one place to another. Robert decided to run after Smith. It was all he could do to keep up with him. Smith

"Mother and Mammy were packing

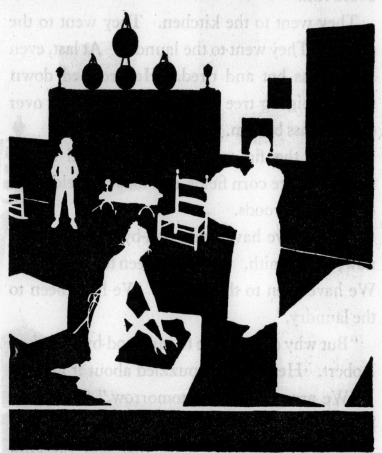

things in boxes and trunks."

could walk faster, almost, than little Robert could run.

They went to the kitchen. They went to the stables. They went to the laundry. At last, even Smith was hot and tired. He dropped down under a big fig tree to rest. Robert rolled over on the grass by him.

Under the fig tree it was cool and shady. Close by were corn fields, and tobacco fields, and cool, green woods.

"I think we have said good-bye to everybody now," said Smith. "We have been to the kitchen. We have been to the stables. We have been to the laundry."

"But why do we have to say good-bye?" asked Robert. He was very puzzled about it all.

"We are going away tomorrow," Smith told him.

Robert brushed off a fly that was buzzing around his nose.

"Why are we going away?" he asked.

"This house is too big," said Smith. "It is old and shabby, and we have no money to fix it."

Robert looked at the house. It *was* a big house, and it *was* old and shabby, but it was home.

"I don't want to go away," said Robert.

"We have to," Smith told him. "If you live in a big house like this, you must have plenty of horses in the stables. You must have plenty of men to work in the fields. You must have plenty of servants in the kitchen. All of that costs a great deal of money. And Father has lost his money."

"Is that why we're going away?"

"That is one reason. There is another one, too."

"What is that?"

"Carter is big enough to go to school. I am almost big enough."

"I am almost big enough, too," said Robert.

"Only there isn't any school here. There is a good school in Alexandria. Carter can go there. I can go there. When you are big enough, you can go there, too."

Robert looked around him. He saw big fields of waving corn, and pine woods that stretched down to the river.

"Are there corn fields in the city?" he asked. He was a very little boy, and had never seen a city.

"Of course not," said Smith.

"Are there pine-tree woods in the city?" asked Robert.

"No, indeed."

Robert liked the fields and woods. He did not want to go to the city. He knew he would feel very strange there. But he asked one more question.

"Will Mother be there?"

"Yes, indeed, Mother will be there."

Right away, Robert was happy again. If Mother was there, he wouldn't feel strange. Everything would be all right.

# III

## FROM STRATFORD TO ALEXANDRIA

### 1. *An Early Start*

IT WAS very early the next morning when Robert awoke. It was so early he thought it must still be night.

Mother, though, was already up and dressed. So was Mammy.

"Come, Marse Robert," said Mammy. "You must git dressed, too."

"The horses are being put to the carriage," said Mother. "We must drive a long way today."

Robert climbed out of his crib. It was a very nice crib. Every time you jounced, it would swing. By kicking up his little heels, a baby could swing himself to sleep.

Robert was no longer a baby, but he still liked

to play in the crib.    It was such fun to jounce up and down.

Today there was no time to play.    When he looked out of the window, he could see the carriage already in front of the house.

Mammy was carrying out big boxes and bundles.    She gave them to Nat.    Nat was the negro servant who drove the horses.    He piled all the boxes and bundles into the carriage.

"I don't believe there will be any room left for us at all," said Smith.    "I hope there isn't.    Then I can ride on top with Nat.    Maybe he will let me drive."

"I want to drive, too," said Robert.

At last they were ready.    Mother and Father were getting into the carriage.    Robert ran back into the house.    He ran into the nursery.    He got down on his fat little knees by the empty fireplace.

The back of the fireplace was made of iron.    It

was decorated with two little angels. They were very black little angels, because they were made of iron, too.

Robert had come back to tell the little angels good-bye. Then he ran out to the carriage. He got in with the others.

Nat folded up the carriage steps. He closed the door. Then he climbed up into the driver's seat. He took the reins in his hands. He cracked his whip.

"Crunch," went the wheels over the road. They were off.

All of the servants came running to the gates. They waved and waved. Robert and Smith leaned out of the window.

"Good-bye!" they called. "Good-bye!"

## 2. *Past Washington's Home*

It was a long way from Stratford to Alexandria. The roads were very bad. Sometimes they were thick with dust. Sometimes there were deep holes. When one of the carriage wheels bumped into a hole, it would almost jounce a very little boy out of his seat.

Sometimes, though, the road was smooth. Sometimes little brooks ran right across it. The horses' feet would go "Splash! Splash!" in the water.

Today, in an automobile, you can go from Stratford to Alexandria in just a few hours. When Robert was a little boy, it took two days.

Robert sat by his mother. He looked out of the carriage window. There were woods on either side of the road.

"Look, Mother!" he cried. "There goes a little squirrel. It ran right in front of the horses!"

Smith was sitting on the other side of the carriage. "I saw a mocking bird!" he called. "It had white marks on its wings!"

They passed fields of tobacco and corn. Then came more woods.

"Over there," said Mrs. Lee, "back of those woods, there was once a beautiful house. It has burned down now. It was called Wakefield.

"When your grandfather's Aunt Hannah's first baby was born at Stratford, there was a baby at Wakefield, too. The baby at Stratford was Richard Henry Lee. He became a very famous man. He was one of those who signed the Declaration of Independence.

"The baby at Wakefield grew up to be a still more famous man. He was——"

"I know who he was!" cried Smith. "He was General George Washington!"

"Yes," said his mother. "And the babies grew into boys, and the boys grew into men, and they were the very best of friends."

"George Washington was my father's friend, too," said Smith.

"Indeed he was. He was one of the best and finest friends your father ever had."

"They asked Father to make a speech about him when he died. Father said that George Washington was 'first in war, first in peace, and first in the hearts of his countrymen.'"

"That is a good thing to remember. Can you say it, too, Robert?"

Robert tried to say it. It had a nice, jingling sound. The wheels of the carriage seemed to say it as they went around and around.

"First in war, first in peace, and first in the hearts of his countrymen."

Robert had waked very early that morning. Before long, he was fast asleep.

## 3. *Robert and the Horses*

When noontime came, they stopped for dinner. They stopped by a little brook that ran across the road. There was a big tree there, with green grass under it.

Nat drove the horses into the middle of the brook, so that they could drink. He gave them some oats for their dinner. Then he led them into the shady woods where it was cool. The horses needed to rest, too.

Robert's family sat under the tree. They brought the cushions from the carriage so that Mother could have a comfortable seat.

Robert watched while they opened the dinner basket. There was cake. There was pie. There was a plate of white beaten biscuit.

Robert thought it was a very good dinner. He did not know why his mother looked sad. He did not know that it was hard to go from a big house to a little one. He did not know it was hard to have only a little money after you have been used to a great deal. Robert thought this trip was just like a long picnic.

After they had rested a while, they got back into the carriage.

"Crunch, crunch," went the wheels. They were starting off again.

Soon they came to a steep hill. Nat stopped the horses. He opened the carriage door and let down the steps. Father and Smith got out. It is hard for horses to pull a heavy load up a hill. Father and Smith would walk up the hill. That would make the horses' load lighter.

"I am going to get out and walk, too," said Robert.

"The hill is so steep, it will be hard to climb," said Mother. "You would get very tired. You do not need to get out. You are only a little boy."

"But I am heavy," said Robert. "Mammy says so. If I get out, it will make it easier for the horses."

He climbed out of the carriage. He trudged up the hill with the others. It was a hard climb.

"Robert trudged up the

"hill with the others."

His feet grew very tired. He was out of breath when he reached the top. But he was happy because he was sure he had made it easier for the horses.

Nat had stopped the carriage at the top of the hill. He opened the door. Father got in.

"I want to ride on the box with Nat," said Smith.

"So do I," said Robert.

"If Nat will let you, you may," his mother told them.

Nat said both boys could climb up on the box with him.

Smith climbed up by Nat. He helped Robert up. Robert sat between him and Nat.

Nat let Robert take the reins in his own hands. Nat's big hands held the reins over his little ones.

"Look!" cried Robert. "I'm driving!"

The horses, themselves, seemed to know he was

driving. They seemed to know he had climbed the long hill, himself, to help them. They went very carefully.

All of his life, Robert was very fond of horses. And always he was very kind to them, so that the horses were fond of him, too.

# IV

## THE STREETS OF ALEXANDRIA

THE new home at Alexandria was close to the Potomac River, just as Stratford had been, but it was not at all like Stratford. It seemed very strange to Robert. The house was small, and the front door steps went right down to the sidewalk. There were ever so many other houses close by, so that you had to walk a long way before you came to any fields at all.

The streets were paved with cobblestones. What a noise the wagons and carriages made rattling over them! And how many wagons and carriages there were! Robert didn't believe even Smith could count them all.

There were exciting things to do, too, here in the city, that one never did at Stratford. At Stratford, almost everything you had to eat grew

"The front steps went right down to the sidewalk."

right in the fields and woods around you, but, in the city, Mother had to go to market to buy what she wanted for dinner.

"Would you like to go with me?" she asked Robert one morning.

Robert did want to, very much indeed. He trotted along by her side down the narrow sidewalk. Old Nat walked behind them with a big basket to take home the things they bought.

At the first corner, there was a deep well.

"Has it always been here?" asked Robert.

"No indeed," said Mother. "Not very many years ago, people who had no wells in their own yards had to go a long way to get water. Even then, it was not always good. Then George Washington had deep wells dug at street corners all through the city. Now people can get good fresh water all the time."

Robert kept tight hold of his mother's hand. He peeped down into the well. It was very deep and dark, and gave him a funny feeling in his throat. Away down at the bottom, he could see something shining and silvery.

A negro woman came to draw up some water. She let the bucket down, down, into the well. At last, they heard a splash. Then she drew the bucket up, filled to the top with clear, cold water.

The water splashed over the sides of the bucket. It ran down on the cobblestones in the street.

The woman poured the water into her pitcher. Then she lifted the pitcher, and put it on top of her head. She held her head so carefully that not a drop of water spilled. Robert watched her go into a house farther down the street. He was glad she had a good well so near her home.

At the next corner, there was an old cannon. Robert wanted to stop there, too. He was sure he could climb to the very top of the cannon, if Mother would only wait.

"No," said Mother. "We haven't time now. We must hurry if we want to get to market and back before the sun grows hot."

# V

## AT THE MARKET

AT LAST they reached the market place. Robert thought he had never seen so many people. Some of the farmers had driven all night to get a good place in the market.

Their carts were backed up against the wall. Under the brick arches of the courthouse, there were tables piled high with fruits and vegetables. There were crates of chickens and ducks. There were pails of berries and baskets of eggs.

Everyone was talking at once. Each one wanted you to buy from him.

"I got good, fat chickens, lady!"

"Buy my nice, sweet corn!"

Robert's mother stopped to talk with them all. She looked at the chickens. She felt the corn, to see if it was tender.

She bought two chickens. She bought some tender, sweet corn. While she paid for them, Nat put them in his big basket.

There was a negro woman with a big pail full of daisies and other flowers.

Robert leaned over them close, to see if they had any odor. The yellow pollen dusted his nose.

A farmer's wife at the next table laughed at him. Then she held out a big pear.

"Look, Sonny," she said. "Here's a nice, ripe pear for you."

Robert forgot about the daisies. He took the ripe pear.

"Thank you," said Robert.

"Whose little boy are you?" asked the woman.

An old man had come up behind her.

"Why, don't you know?" he asked. "He is Light-Horse Harry Lee's son."

"Oh!" said the woman. She turned to a big

" 'I get good fat

CLOTILDE EMBREE FUNK

chickens, lady!'"

girl standing by the table. "Look! That is Light-Horse Harry Lee's little boy."

You could see she thought it was a fine thing to be Light-Horse Harry Lee's little boy. So did the big girl. So did Robert. He felt very proud.

"The name of Lee is a fine old name," said the old man. "Everyone in Virginia knows it. It is a name to be trusted. You must take good care of it, Sonny."

Robert laughed. It sounded funny to talk about taking care of a *name!*

As he grew older, though, he began to understand. For nearly two hundred years, the Lees of Virginia had been truthful and honest gentlemen. They had been men whom you could trust. Their name had come to stand for what they stood for. Now it was *his* name, and he must take care of it. He, too, must be truthful and honest. He must keep it a name people could trust.

He did that all his life. Once, when he was an

old man, and had lost everything he owned, some people offered him a great deal of money if he would come into their business. They did not want him to do any work. They wanted to use his name. He was a famous man then. They knew everybody in Virginia, and all through the South, would say, "If General Lee is in this business, it is safe for us to put our money in it."

But he would not go into their business, or take their money. He did not want them to use his name. He had kept it a fine name all his life, and he was still taking care of it. When he died, he had very little money to leave his children, but he left them a name that was even finer than it had been when it first became his. It was more admired and loved than ever.

# VI

## 1. *What Shall We Play?*

THE old man in the market place was not
the only one who knew Father. Many of
the soldiers who had been in the army with him
came from Alexandria. Some of them still lived
there. They were old men now, but they still
liked to tell about the things Light-Horse Harry
had done.

Robert and Smith liked to listen, too. Espe-
cially did they like the story about Father at
Paulus Hook. They thought it was one of the
best of all the stories the old soldiers told them.

The enemy had a strong fort at Paulus Hook
during the Revolution. They thought it was so
strong it couldn't be taken. But Father and his

44

men had crept up on them very, very quietly at night. They had crossed water up to their waists. Then, all of a sudden, they had rushed on the fort. The enemy had been so surprised, they had to give in.

It made a fine game. Robert and Smith were playing it one morning on the porch. They piled up all the chairs at one end to make a "fort." As they played they took turns being Father.

The one who was playing the "enemy" would crawl under the chairs and pretend that he was asleep. The other would come creeping across the porch very, very quietly until he was close to the "fort." Then he would give a yell, and try to drag his brother out from the "fort."

It was a fine game, but it was noisy. Robert wasn't surprised when Ann came to the door.

"Please don't make such a fuss!" she said. "The baby has just gone to sleep."

Robert was no longer the youngest child in the

"Creeping across the

Lee family. There was a baby sister named Mildred now. Robert thought she was a very nice baby. He did wish, though, that she wouldn't always go to sleep when he wanted to make a noise, and make a noise when he wanted to go to sleep.

"Why don't you play some quiet game?" asked Ann.

porch very, very quietly."

Robert and Smith sat down on the porch step.
They tried hard to think of some quiet game.
Robert looked down the street.  He saw Father
coming.

"I know!" cried Robert, jumping up.  "We
won't play any game at all. We'll get Father
to tell us a story."

The two boys ran to meet their father.  Ann

went back into the house for her workbox. She liked to hear Father's stories, too.

Girls, though, were not supposed to sit with empty hands. There were no sewing machines, then. All the clothes worn by everybody in the family had to be made by hand. That meant that little girls must be taught to sew just as soon as their fingers were big enough to hold a needle. They kept on with their sewing until they were old women.

Today, Ann was stitching some ruffles for her father's neck-cloth.

She brought her workbox out to the porch. She had already started when Father came up.

Smith pulled a chair for his father to the side of the porch, where he could catch the breeze. Robert took his big, white hat and long cane. Then they sat on the porch steps.

"Now tell us a story, please," said Robert.

"About the war," said Smith.

"I'd like a story with a woman in it," said Ann.

"Women don't fight," Smith told her.

"But they love their country just the same as men do, don't they, Father?"

"Of course they do," said her father. "It isn't enough just to be willing to fight for your country. You must love it so that you are ready to give up anything you have if your country needs it."

"Women can do that," said Ann.

"I know one woman who did," said Father.

## 2. *The Story of Mrs. Motte*

"The woman's name," said Father, "was Mrs. Motte. Before the war, she lived in a beautiful home, high up on a hill.

"Then the enemy came. They thought her home would make a good fort. They took it away from her. She had nowhere to go except a very little house over on the next hill. Her husband was dead. She had no one to help her."

"Poor Mrs. Motte!" said Ann.

"But you got her house back for her, didn't you, Father?" asked Smith.

Father shook his head. "I tried to. If we could get our soldiers up close to the house before they were fired on, I was sure we could drive the enemy out. We started to dig a deep ditch, so that we could creep up close to the house.

"We had left men back on the road to watch. Suddenly one of them came riding up as fast as he could.

" 'There is a large army on the way to help the soldiers in the fort,' he told us.

"That was very bad. If we couldn't get the men out of the fort before this help got there, we would have the fort on one side of us, and an army on the other. We would be shot to pieces.

"We didn't have time to finish the ditch. There

was only one thing to do. Instead of helping Mrs. Motte to get her house back, we would have to burn it down.

"She had been very kind to us. I hated to tell her what we would have to do. But, when she heard it, what do you think she said?"

"She begged you not to burn her home."

"No, indeed. She said, 'If burning my house will help my country, I shall be glad to have it burned.'

"She went into the little house where she was living then. She brought back a bow and some arrows. 'You can use these,' she said.

"We set fire to one of the arrows. When it was blazing, we shot it into the roof of Mrs. Motte's beautiful home.

"The sun had dried the roof so that it caught fire quickly. We shot a second blazing arrow. We shot a third blazing arrow. Soon the whole roof was on fire.

"The enemy had to come out. We took them prisoners. We had won the fight, but Mrs. Motte's home was burned down."

"What did she do then?" asked Robert.

"She invited as many of our prisoners and ourselves as the little house would hold, to dinner. It was the very best dinner we had had for many a day."

"She was a real patriot," said Robert.

"Yes," said Father, "I think so, too."

# VII

## A SOLDIER'S SON MUST BE BRAVE

### 1. *What Is a Mob?*

ROBERT was "going on six years old" now.
He was old enough to go walking with
Father.  He liked to go down to the river and
watch the boats with their big, white sails.  He
liked to go to the square where Washington used
to drill his soldiers.

One morning, Father met a friend there. They
talked, and talked, until Robert got very tired.

It made him feel very uncomfortable, too, to
see how excited Father was getting.  His face
was very red.  He pounded the sidewalk with
his cane.

"I tell you, Sir," said Father, "no man should
ever give in to a mob!"

Robert wondered what a "mob" was.  He asked Mother when he got home.

"A mob," said Mother, "is a crowd of people who have become so angry and excited that they often do cruel and wicked things.  Sometimes they even kill people before they can be stopped."

"Father wouldn't give in to any mob," said Robert.  "He would stop it."

"He would try to," Mrs. Lee agreed.

Smith came into the room just in time to hear them.  "Even a mob would listen to Father," said Smith.  "He was George Washington's friend.  He has been Governor of Virginia. They would remember how he fought in the Revolution."

Mother shook her head.  "A mob forgets things like that.  But you boys must never forget. You must always remember that you are the sons of a brave soldier, and you must be very brave, too."

## 2.  *Father Is Hurt*

It was a very beautiful world outdoors. Blackberries were ripe. The honeysuckle was blooming. Robert forgot all about mobs.

Father went to Baltimore. Smith and Robert waved good-bye to him. The baby was in the hall. They tried to make her wave good-bye, too.

He was gone for nearly a week. Then, one day, a gentleman came riding down the street on horseback. He asked for Mrs. Lee. He talked with her for a long time. When he left, Robert saw that his mother was crying.

"Mother, dear!" cried Robert, "what is the matter?"

Mother put her arm around Robert. As she bent over him, he felt something hot and wet fall on his hair.

"Your father has been badly hurt," said Mother. "An angry mob wanted to kill one of

his friends. When he tried to stop them, they
tried to kill him, too."

"Will he get well?" Robert asked.

"I don't know," said his mother, "but we shall
nurse him ever so carefully—all of us."

### 3.  *Father Goes Away*

After a long time they brought Father home.
He was very badly hurt. All day long he lay in
his big bed. The bed had four posts and a top.
Curtains were hung from the top and tied back

"He gave her his smooth brown horse-chestnuts to play with"

against the posts. It made the bed look like a little room all by itself.

Robert soon found out that, when there is a sick person in the house, there is a great deal of work to be done.

He ran errands for Mother. He tended the baby so that Mammy could help nurse Father. He let her play with his ball to keep her from crying. He gave her his very own smooth, brown horse-chestnuts to play with.

He learned to play very quietly, himself, so that Father could sleep.

But Father didn't get any better. Perhaps, if he could go to some hot, sunny place away down South, it would help.

So, once more, the children stood in the hall to tell him good-bye.

"You will have to take care of Mother while I am away," he told them.

"We shall," they promised.

They watched Nat help Father into the car-riage. It drove away toward the river.

"Good-bye, good-bye!" they called.

There was a big lump in Robert's throat. Mother was crying. Ann was crying. Robert wanted to cry, too.

But he remembered that he was a soldier's son, and a soldier's son must be brave. Besides, he had promised to take care of Mother.

Robert swallowed very, very hard. He couldn't cry, now.

# VIII

## ROBERT LEARNS TO READ

NOT long after Father went away, Smith started to school at the Academy. The Academy was a school for big boys. Robert was too young to go there yet.

He must learn to read first, and to write, and to work sums on his slate. Like many other little boys in Alexandria, he would learn all this at home. Mother would be his first teacher.

Every morning, as soon as breakfast was over, Nat would bring a little tub of hot water into the dining room. He would put it on the table in front of Mother. Mother would carefully wash the silver teapot, the sugar dish, and the thin cups and saucers that were too precious to be sent out to the kitchen.

Robert could go out and play while this was

going on.  Spec, the dog, would be waiting for him out in the yard.  They would chase up and down together, and have a fine time.

Soon, though, Mother would call from the doorway, "Come, Robert, it is time for your lesson."

Of course, Robert wanted to learn to read.  He didn't want to grow up like Old John, down by the river.  Nat said Old John was "poor white trash."  He was a grown man, but he couldn't even write his own name.  He had to make a crossmark, and get somebody else to write by it, for him, "John—his mark."

No, Robert didn't want to grow up like that, but it was hard to have to go inside, when there were so many things to do outdoors.

Spec was begging him to stay out and play.  He knew, if he went down to the stable, Nat would let him help take care of the horses. Horses and dogs were much more fun than books.

But Mother was calling again.

"I'll come back as soon as I can," Robert told Spec.

Spec wagged his tail. Then he curled up by the door to wait for Robert.

Robert went inside. He hung up his cap. He went into his mother's room.

It was such a cool morning, Nat had built a fire in the big, open fireplace. Robert took his book and sat down on a footstool by the fire.

Mother sat close by. She was knitting a stocking for Robert.

I don't believe you would have liked Robert's book at all.

There were only a few pictures. The print was very small. The leaves were fastened together so tightly that it was hard to hold the book open. It had thin, wooden boards for covers. The boards were covered with blue paper.

On the first page of this blue-backed speller

"Mrs. Lee pointed with her knitting needle."

was a picture of George Washington. The next page showed the letters of the alphabet. Robert knew them all, now. He pointed them out to Mother with a pin.

"Big A, little a. Big B, little b."

"Good," said Mother. "Now we can start on the next page."

The next page was filled with rows of letters put together.

ab  eb  ib  ob  ub

ac  ec  ic  oc  uc

They didn't make any sense at all, but children were supposed to learn them before they began to spell words. Then the teacher could be sure they knew their letters.

Mrs. Lee pointed with her knitting needle to the first letters.

"A—b," said Mrs. Lee, "ab."

"A—b," said Robert after her, "ab."

It wasn't a very interesting way to learn to read

"Have children always had books just like this to start with?" asked Robert.

"No, indeed," said Mother. "Not so long ago, most of them used what were called hornbooks— only they really weren't books at all."

"What were they?" asked Robert.

"Well, a hornbook looked something like a hand-mirror. It had just such a handle, but instead of the mirror, there was a piece of paper, with all the letters on it, and the Lord's Prayer. The paper was covered by a piece of horn so thin you could see through it. That kept the paper from getting mussed up, you see. Then there was a string so that you could tie it around your waist instead of carrying it."

Robert laughed. It must have looked funny to see children running around with their hornbooks dangling from their waists.

Mother was smiling, too. "Once, I heard of a teacher who made gingerbread letters to put in side the hornbook. Then, when the children had learned it, they could eat their lesson up."

Ann came into the room just then. She heard what Mother was saying.

"I came past the kitchen just now," said Ann. "Maybe it wasn't gingerbread letters I smelled, but I think it was right good gingerbread, just the same. And it smelled as if it would be done just about when you finished your lesson."

Robert picked up his book in a hurry.

Mother pointed with her needle.

"E—b, eb," said Mother.

"E—b, eb," said Robert.

You should have seen how quickly that lesson was finished!

In almost no time at all, Robert was out in the yard again. He had a big piece of gingerbread in his hand. Spec was jumping up and down. He was barking quick, short barks.

Robert gave him a piece of gingerbread. Then

they ran down the yard together. They ran out to the stable to see how the horses were getting along.

## IX

## NEWS FROM LAKE ERIE

### 1. *Robert Hears the News*

ROBERT was playing horse with the baby. She sat in his wagon while he pulled it around the room. Now he would go slow. Now he would go fast. Now he would stamp his feet. The floor was bare. He made a fine noise when he stamped. Bang! Bang!

"Boom!"

That was not Robert's feet. It was a bigger

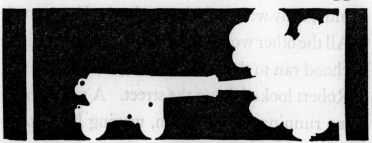

"Boom!"

noise than he could make. It came from out-
doors. "Boom!"

"Mother!" called Robert. "What is that?"

Mother came hurrying through the hall. "It
is the cannon!" she cried. "There's been news of
some battle."

She picked up Mildred and ran to the front
door. Robert ran with her. He was very excited.

The United States had been at war with England for more than a year. History books now
call it the War of 1812.

Big Brother Henry was in the Army. So were
the brothers of many of his friends. Robert
could hardly wait to find out what had happened.

All the other women and children in the neigh-
borhood ran to their front doors, too.

Robert looked down the street. A young man
came running toward them, waving his hat.

"Hurrah!" he cried, "Hurrah!"

"What is it?" called Robert.

"We have met the enemy and they are ours!"

"Where? When? Who?"

Everybody crowded around him. He was so out of breath he could hardly talk.

"The news has just come. Lieutenant Perry has fought with the British fleet on Lake Erie. That is what the message says. 'We have met the enemy and they are ours.'"

"Hurrah!" cried Robert.

"Boom! Boom!" went the cannon, as if it, too, were crying, "Hurrah! Hurrah!"

The young man started off up the street. Robert ran along with him.

"Hurrah!" he called to everybody he saw. "We have met the enemy and they are ours."

## 2.   *What Is a Hero?*

Robert was tired when he got back home.   So
was Smith. He had just come in, too. They were
both still excited.

"As soon as I am old enough," said Smith, "I
shall go into the Navy.  I want to be like Lieutenant Perry.  He is a great hero.  A hero always
wins."

"Not always," said Mother.   "Don't you remember, last summer, when Captain Lawrence's
ship fought with the British ship, outside Bos-
ton?"

"Yes, indeed!" said Smith.

"Captain Lawrence's ship was lost, and he was
killed," Smith said.   "But he died fighting.   His
last words were, 'Don't give up the ship.' "

"Wasn't he a hero?" asked Mother.

"Of course he was."

"But he didn't win."

Robert thought about that.

"He was always brave, and he tried his very hardest. I suspect that was why he was a hero."

"I suspect so, too," said Mother.

When Robert was a man, he, too, fought in a sad war. He did not win, but always he was brave, and he tried his very hardest. He, too, was a hero.

## X

## ROBERT GOES CALLING

### 1. *A Present for Mildred*

"I'SE gwine to Arlington to take a letter to Mrs. Custis." Old Nat stood at the door. "If I knew a white boy what promised to mind real good, I might take him with me."

"Oh, you do!" cried Robert, jumping up. "Doesn't he, Mother? Please take me, Nat."

"Is your Ma willing?" asked Nat.

Mother nodded, and Robert ran to get ready. Baby Mildred began to cry. She wanted to go, too.

"You can't go," Robert told Mildred. "You're too little. You'd get tired and cold. But you mustn't cry. When I come back, I'll bring you a present."

Mildred stopped crying. She knew Robert would keep his promise.

Old Nat climbed up on the box with Robert. He slapped the reins over the horses' backs. Away they went.

The air was so cold Robert's fingers tingled. He slapped his hands together to make them warm.

"I reckon Jack Frost came last night," said Nat. "He can bite a body's fingers almost off. There is something else he did, too."

They were driving past a great sweet gum tree. All summer long its leaves had been green. To-day they were bright red.

"Oh, stop, Nat!" cried Robert. "Let me get some red leaves. They will make a fine present for Mildred."

Nat wouldn't stop. "Just you wait," he said. "I'll show you a present what's finer than that, what Jack Frost has fixed for Miss Mildred."

"What is it?" asked Robert.

Nat shook his head. "Just you wait," was all he would say.

Robert puzzled for a little while, but soon he forgot all about it. He was too busy enjoying everything that he saw.

They drove past fields where the grass was stiff with frost. They drove along the Potomac River, where wild ducks were bobbing up and down with the ripples on the water. It was Virginia, and it was home! Robert loved it when he was a little boy. He loved it all his life.

## 2. *A Morning Call*

At last, they came to a steep hill. At the top of the hill was a big house. It was as big as Stratford, and not even Stratford had such fine large pillars in front. Robert had never before seen anything like them.

Nat drove up the steep hill. He stopped in front of the big pillars. Then he climbed down from his seat.

There was a big brass knocker on the door of the house. Nat lifted it and knocked. It sounded so loud Robert was afraid the horses would be frightened.

A negro servant opened the door. He took the letter Nat handed him.

**Arlington**

Just then a little girl came up. She was about as old as Robert. She had golden hair and bright eyes.

Robert knew her very well. She was Mary Custis.

"You must come in and get warm," she told Nat. "Oh, there is Robert! He must come in and get warm, too."

Old Nat went out to the kitchen to warm his feet before the big kitchen fire. Robert went into the hall with Mary.

He always liked to come to Arlington. Mary's father was George Washington's adopted son. There were many things here in the house that had once belonged to Washington. There were the cups and saucers he had used. There was the bed on which he had slept.

There were even some of the clothes that he had worn.

Mary showed Robert all of these things. He

was having such a good time he forgot his feet were cold. By the time he remembered them, they had grown warm all by themselves.

By that time, Nat was warm, too.

He sent word into the hall that, if young Marse Robert was ready, they'd better be going.

Mary stood at the door, to wave good-bye.

"That's a mighty fine little lady," said Nat.

"Um-hum," said Robert. He wasn't interested in little ladies very much right then. He did not know that someday he would come riding to Arlington to marry Mary Custis. He did not know that his own children would live in this big house on top of the hill.

Suddenly he remembered something.

"Please, Nat," he said, "we haven't found the present for Mildred, yet."

"Just you wait," said the old man. "Just you wait."

CLOTILDE EMBREE FUNK

Mary showed him George

Washington's cups and saucers.

### 3. *Nuts and Turkeys*

Robert waited. At last they came to a big clump of trees.

"I reckon," said the old man, "you might find her a present in there. And, while you're hunting one way, I'll be hunting another."

He stopped the horses. He and Robert climbed down.

"You go that way, and I'll go this."

Robert started into the woods. How could he find the present, when he didn't know where to look?

He looked up at the tops of the tall trees. He looked at the dead leaves on the ground. Then he saw some very small trees. They were filled with big, prickly burs. Yesterday you couldn't have touched them without hurting your fingers. Jack Frost could touch them, though. He had pricked each one open with his sharp fingers.

Inside was a little brown nut. It looked like a very small chestnut.

"Hurrah!" cried Robert. "Chinkapins!"

He popped one into his mouth. The shell was so thin, he could bite into it with his sharp teeth. Oh, but it was good!

Robert began to gather the chinkapins as fast as ever he could.

When he had his cap nearly full, Nat came back. Nat was excited, too.

"Marse Robert," he said, "what do you think I saw? A wild turkey. Yes, sir. A turkey. I'se going home to get my gun. If your Ma will just let me stop work to go a-hunting, we'll have turkey for dinner tomorrow."

Mildred was taking her nap when they got home. Robert showed the pretty chinkapins to Ann.

"How splendid!" said Ann. "But we mustn't give them to the baby like that. She would put them in her mouth and swallow them whole. Wait a minute."

Ann got a sharp needle. She threaded it with a strong thread. Then she strung the chinkapins on the thread as if they were big brown beads.

"There! Now we'll see what Baby Mildred thinks of that. Listen! She's waking up now."

Robert ran to Mildred's crib. The little girl was just sitting up. He threw the chinkapin necklace over her head.

My, but Mildred was pleased! So was Mother.

"It is a fine present," said Mother.

"It's part a present from me," said Robert, "and part from Nat, and part from Jack Frost."

"Didn't you bring me a present?" teased Ann.

"I brought you a secret," said Robert. He came close and whispered in her ear:

"We are going to have wild turkey for dinner tomorrow. Nat and I are going hunting."

# XI

## HOLLY AND MISTLETOE

IT WAS the week before Christmas. Smith's classes at the Academy had stopped. Robert's lessons with Mother had stopped. The Lee family was on its way to Cousin William Fitzhugh's for Christmas.

"I wish it hadn't snowed Monday," said Robert.

Robert liked snow. He liked to see it coming down. He liked to make snow balls and snow forts, and to go sliding downhill.

In Virginia, though, the snow doesn't stay on the ground very long. It usually melts in two or three days.

That was what had happened now. Already, the fields were bare again. The melted snow had filled the holes in the road with water. It had turned the road, itself, into soft and slushy mud.

That was why Robert was sorry it had snowed. The wheels of the carriage sank deep in the mud. The horses' feet sank deep, too. They had to pull and tug with all their strength, to pull the carriage through the mud.

Once Robert was sure they were stuck. Nat climbed down from his seat. He and the boys cut poles in the woods on the side of the road. They put these in front of the wheels. Then Nat clucked to the horses. Oh, how they tugged! At last the carriage moved.

It was late when they reached Cousin William's. They were all tired and hungry. Robert fell asleep almost before he could get into bed.

The next morning, though, he was up bright and early. It was the day before Christmas. The air was crisp and cold. When he went past the big kitchen, he could smell pie and turkey cooking.

The house was full of people. There were the folk who always lived there. There were the visiting aunts and uncles and cousins. Then there were all the servants. On the day before Christmas, though, there was enough to do to keep everybody busy.

The young people, first, went to gather the Christmas greens. How Robert enjoyed that! They rode in a big wagon until they came to a place where the woods were thick with holly trees. Running cedar trailed over the ground.

Robert and his cousins gathered great armloads of the running cedar. They broke off branches of holly. They filled the wagon until there was no room for them to get back in. Then they walked along by it, to the little country church.

They filled the windows of the church with holly. They trimmed the walls with running cedar. The little church looked very beautiful, indeed.  Then they went back to the woods for another load.

They would trim the big hall and the ballroom at Cousin William's with this.

Two or three little negroes had come down into the woods with the "white folks."  One of them ran up to Robert as they were on their way home.

"Look, Marse Robert!" he said.  He pointed up into a big tree.

Robert looked up into the tree.  Its leaves were all gone.  Through the bare branches you could see a thick clump of something near the top. Robert thought, for a minute, that it was just a bird's old nest, filled with dead leaves.  Then he whistled.

"Mistletoe!" said Robert.

"Yes, suh!" said the little negro.  "I'se gwine to get it."

He put his arms around the tree.  He dug his knees and toes into the thick bark.  The next

"Robert stood underneath."

minute he was climbing up the tree like a little monkey.

Robert stood underneath and waited until he reached the mistletoe.

"Is you there, Marse Robert?" called the little negro.

"Right here."

"Here she comes!" cried the little negro.

If the mistletoe fell on the ground, its soft white berries might be mashed. He dropped it right into Robert's hands.

Then he scampered down from the tree. Robert gave him the mistletoe.

The others had gone on ahead. The little negro ran after them.

"Hi-yi!" he called. "I got some mistletoe."

Everybody laughed. They always wanted a piece of mistletoe to hang in the hall at Christmas. If a boy found a girl standing under it, he would try to kiss her. It was part of the Christmas fun.

"Here," said one of the big cousins, "that's fine."

He took the mistletoe from the little negro, and gave him a big silver dollar.

The little negro grinned all over his face. He thought that was fine, too.

Then they all hurried home to decorate the big hall with the cedar, the holly, and the mistletoe.

## XII

## CHRISTMAS DAY

THE servants had a dance that night, down in the barn. Robert and some of the other boys went to watch them for a while. One negro played a banjo; another played a fiddle. Such jigging and dancing were going on, that the boys could hardly pull themselves away.

Up at the big house, though, the older boys were setting off fire-works. There were torpedo crackers and pinwheels, and Roman candles. Of course, everybody wanted to help with those.

It was late before the children got to bed that night, but that fact didn't keep them from waking early the next morning. There was no Christmas tree, but they all had Christmas stockings, filled to the very top. What talking and laughing there was as all the children tried to show their stockings to one another at the same time! It was hard to put those stockings down, even for breakfast.

Almost as soon as breakfast was over, it was time to start to church. Some people drove over in carriages; others rode on horseback. Many of the boys walked. But everybody went. What difference did it make if there wasn't any fire in the church? They could bundle up well, and the women could carry little foot stoves to keep their toes from getting too cold.

The church looked very beautiful with all of its green trimmings. The cedar filled it with a Christmasy odor.

Robert knelt by his mother as they prayed. The Christ child seemed very real to him.

The long walk back in the clear, cold air gave everybody a good appetite for dinner.

And what a dinner! Everything that Robert liked best! What pies and cakes! What a big

"They all had

CLOTILDE
EMBREE
FUNK

Christmas stockings."

plum pudding! It wasn't a dinner to be eaten in a hurry. It lasted until the sun began to go down and it was time for the ladies to start dressing for the dance.

Mother said Robert could sit up for a while after the dance began. Most of the other mothers told their children the same thing. The children sat on the steps out in the hall.

There they could see the company when they came. First there would be a loud "Rap! Rap!" on the knocker. Pompey, the big negro servant, opened the door, to let in a gust of cold air. There was a flurry of wind that set all the hall candles to winking. Then the company came gaily in. The ladies went upstairs to take off their cloaks and hoods. The men warmed themselves by the blazing fire in the hall.

At last the ladies came downstairs. They all went into the ballroom.

Robert and the other children on the

stairs could look down into the ballroom, too. They could hear the gay music of the violins. They could see the ladies bow low to their partners in the dance.

Robert could hear the little girls whispering about when *they* would be old enough to go to dances. Robert thought it wouldn't be so bad to go to a dance, himself.

They had all been up early that morning. They had been busy all day. It wasn't long before they began to get sleepy. Of course, they pretended they weren't. They all said to their mothers, "Oh, *please* let us stay up a little longer."

Really, though, their eyes were so nearly shut they could hardly get upstairs. Robert went to sleep twice before he had finished undressing But hadn't it been a fine Christmas?

# XIII

## A NEW SONG

THE war went on for nearly a year after Robert first heard the cannon, but it was all so far away that sometimes he almost forgot about it. When hot summer came again, though, he could no longer forget. A terrible thing happened.

Just a few miles away from Robert's home, right across the Potomac River from the home of Mary Custis, was the city of Washington. It was named for George Washington. It was the capital of the United States. It was a very new city, and a very beautiful one.

That summer the British began to march on Washington. Every day they came nearer and nearer. At last, one afternoon, Smith called to Robert.

"Come," he said, "the boys have all gone down to the river. There is something to see there."

Robert went with him 'to the river bank. "Look," said Smith.

Far up the river, on the other side, was a great cloud of smoke.

"What is it?" asked Robert.

"The city of Washington is burning. The British have set fire to it. They have burned the Capitol building. They have burned the house where the President lives. The whole city is burning."

Robert could hardly sleep that night. He thought of the poor people whose homes were burning. The war wasn't far away any more. It was very close. And it wasn't just exciting. It was horrible.

The next morning, he wanted to go back to the river right away, to see if he could still see the smoke.

Mother said, "No. We must none of us go out of the house today."

"Why not?" asked Robert. It seemed hard to stay inside when so much was going on out-doors.

"The British warships are coming up the river," said Mother. "Maybe they will set fire to Alexandria as they did to Washington. Wo-men and children must stay off the streets."

The warships stopped right opposite Alex-andria. Their guns were aimed at the court house, and the market place, and the houses close by the river.

A British Warship

But they did not fire. Their captain sent a message instead.

"If you will give us the cotton and flour that you have stored up, we shall not burn your city."

The people of Alexandria gave them sixteen thousand barrels of flour. They gave them the cotton. The warships went back down the river.

"Where will they go now?" asked Robert.

"They will probably try to take Baltimore."

"But there is a fort outside Baltimore. Will they be able to get past that? Will they get past the fort, Mother?"

Robert felt that he couldn't stand it if they burned Baltimore, too.

Mother looked worried. "I don't know," she said. "We'll have to wait and see."

Robert was worried, too. He had cousins who lived in Baltimore. Suppose their home should be burned. Oh, if only the fort could hold out! Could it? *Could it?*

It was two weeks before the answer came to Alexandria.  The answer was, "Yes."

All night the British warships tried to get past Fort McHenry, but the soldiers in the fort held them off.  When morning came, the American flag was still flying there, and the warships had to give up and go back.  Soon after that, the War of 1812 was over.

How happy everybody in Alexandria was when they heard the news that the soldiers in Fort McHenry had kept the enemy back!  Robert was very happy, too.

He ran up and down the streets, with Spec at his heels, calling to all the boys he knew.

It was not long after that, that everywhere Robert went, he heard people singing a new song.  It didn't take Robert long to learn it, too.

He liked the tune of it.  He liked the words. He liked the shivery feeling it sent down his back every time he sang it.

"Listen, Mother!" he called. "I know a song. It is a fine song! Everyone is singing it."

"Where did it come from?" asked Mrs. Lee.

"There was a man watching the fight at Fort McHenry. He wrote the song while he watched. It's a grand song. Listen, Mother."

Every boy and girl today knows the song that Robert began to sing. After a hundred years, we still like it as much as he did. It was "The Star Spangled Banner."

"The star spangled banner, oh, long may it wave
O'er the land of the free and the home of the brave!"

## XIV

## AT BROTHER HENRY'S

BROTHER Henry had been a grown man when Robert was born. Soon after the war was over, he was married, and he and his wife went to live at Stratford.

"I shall always be glad to have my young brothers visit me," he told Mrs. Lee. "Let them come whenever they want to."

Robert liked to go to Stratford. Alexandria was a very nice city, but the houses were very close together. Boys mustn't fly kites in the streets because they might frighten the horses. They couldn't play bandy there, either.

The houses weren't close together at Stratford. The nearest neighbor was so far away you couldn't hear his roosters crow. You never got lonesome, though, because there was always company—company to dinner, company to spend the night, company to spend the week, or maybe two or three months.

Sometimes there were men who came on horseback. Sometimes there were ladies who drove up in big coaches. Sometimes the ladies brought their children with them.

One day a girl cousin stepped down out of a carriage. She was very glad to see Robert.

"I was so afraid there wouldn't be any children here," she said. "It's the first time I have ever been to Stratford. You must show me everything. Where shall we start?"

"Do you want to go upstairs to the dining room, or downstairs to the bedrooms?" asked Robert.

"The dining room upstairs, and the bedrooms downstairs!" laughed the girl cousin. "That's a funny way to build a house."

Robert laughed, too. "And the kitchen's out

in the front yard—only, really, it is a little house all by itself, with a yard of its own, and a fence all around it. Come see."

The girl cousin shook her head. "The kitchen's the nicest. Let's save that until last."

Robert showed her the angels in the back of the nursery fireplace. He showed her the big chest that had come from England, shaped like a boat, so that it would float if the big boat that brought it were shipwrecked. He showed her the narrow stairs going up into the attic.

They squeezed up them, and went out on the roof. There they could look away off down the river. A good stiff breeze was blowing.

"This breeze makes me hungry," said Robert. "Now let's go to the kitchen."

They slipped through the gate that led to the kitchen yard. A little negro boy sat there on a bench, shelling beans. Never, in all his life, had

Robert ever seen anyone shell beans quite so slowly.

"I think he is asleep," said the girl cousin.

Big, black Cindy, the cook, came to the door.

"You, George Washington Perkins," she called. "You better hustle."

"Yas'm," The boy's fingers moved faster—but only until Cindy turned back into the kitchen. Then he looked up at the children and grinned.

"Aunt Cindy, she's right smart cross this morning. Yes, suh!"

"Well, I hope, myself," said Robert, "that those beans are for tomorrow's dinner instead of today's."

"Maybe, if Aunt Cindy's so cross, we'd better not go in," said the girl cousin.

"Oh, she won't mind, so long as we don't get underfoot. I want you to see things."

They crossed the kitchen yard and peeped in at the big door.

There was no stove in the kitchen, but the room was good and hot, just the same. No wonder! All across one side of the wall was a big fireplace—so big that Robert and the girl cousin and half a dozen other children could have stood inside it.

No one wanted to stand inside it now, though. One would have roasted oneself brown in a jiffy in the big fire that took up nearly all the space.

Big pots of things that bubbled and steamed hung over the fire. Corn was roasting in one corner. There was an oven, banked by hot coals, where golden corn-bread was baking. A whole row of pies had just come out of the oven and were smoking hot, sizzling with rich fruit juice.

In one corner of the kitchen was a wooden block. There was a batch of dough on the block.

Another little negro boy was pounding it with a hammer.

"Yum, yum!" said the girl cousin. "Beaten biscuit for supper."

Aunt Cindy turned and saw them. "You white chil'len get out of here," she said crossly. "I ain't got time to bother with you-all."

"Now, please, Aunt Cindy," said Robert. "We're hungry. Can't you give us just a little snack to last us until dinner time?"

There was a pan of gingerbread on the table. Aunt Cindy broke off two big pieces.

"Now you-all clear out," she said.

The two children went back into the kitchen yard. The little negro still sat on the bench, but he wasn't shelling beans. He was fast asleep.

"You'd better wake up," said the girl cousin. "Aunt Cindy will get you!"

Robert slipped a piece of the gingerbread into his hand. Then they went on.

"I'm thirsty," said the girl cousin. "Let's get something to drink, too, before we eat."

They went to the spring house, where a negro woman was churning butter. She was better natured than Aunt Cindy. She took a gourd dipper down from the wall, and gave them each a long drink of buttermilk.

There was a horse-chestnut tree in the garden.

**A Long Drink of Buttermilk**

Robert liked it best of all the trees because his mother had planted it.  They sat down there to eat their gingerbread.

Now it was almost time for Aunt Cindy to send the dinner to the big house.

"Let's stay here and watch," said the girl cousin.  "We don't have to go in yet."

She knew the children wouldn't have dinner with the grown people.  After a while, they would have a dinner of their own.

A little negro boy stood at the top of the steps that led to the door nearest the dining room.  Another stood half-way up.  Others waited around the kitchen.

Aunt Cindy came to the kitchen door.  She had a large covered platter in her hands.  She gave it to the nearest child.  He carried it across the yard.  He was very proud of his load.  He handed it to the boy on the stairs.  The boy on the stairs passed it to the boy at the top.  The boy at the top passed it to the servant inside. The servant inside took it on into the dining room.

"It is just like handing buckets down the line at a fire," said Robert.

The girl cousin giggled. "Wouldn't you think the things would be cold by the time they reached the dining room?"

Robert shook his head. "Haven't you ever seen a hot water plate? It has two bottoms, with a big space in between, and a hole at one side. Aunt Cindy pours hot water into the hole. The hot water keeps the plate hot a long time."

The little negroes were hurrying back and forth with the plates.

"I do believe," said Robert, "I'm getting hungry all over again."

"Me, too," said the girl cousin. "Maybe we had better go in, after all."

They scampered into the house by another door, to get ready for dinner. And a very good dinner it was.

## XV

## GRANDFATHER CARTER'S HOME

### 1. *Getting Ready*

STRATFORD was not the only place where Robert liked to go a-visiting. There was Shirley, too.

Mother loved Shirley. It was the home where she had been born. She had lived there until she was married. She loved the fine old house. She loved the beautiful garden. So did Robert.

Shirley was one of the finest houses in all Virginia. The very finest houses, though, a hundred years ago, did not have many of the things that you and I expect in only ordinary houses. Robert did not miss them because he didn't even know what they were. You and I would miss them very much. When we want hot water, for instance, to wash our hands, we turn on the faucet marked "hot," and the hot water comes steaming out.

This is what had to happen before Robert could get any hot water:

The servants had to go out to the well and pull up a heavy bucket of water. They had to carry this to the kitchen.   Then they had to go out to the wood-pile, and bring in an armload of wood. They had to build a fire in the fireplace.   Then they poured the water into a kettle and hung it

Shirley

over the fire. When it was hot, they poured it into a pail. Then they carried it over to the big house, and brought it upstairs. Then, at last, Robert could have hot water.

It was the same way with nearly everything else. Where we have electric lights, they had candles which they had to make themselves. Where we use the telephone, they had to send a servant with a note.

Of course, with all this extra work, they needed more servants than we do, today. And at Shirley, there were plenty of servants. Robert could count them by the dozens.

There was plenty of company, too. Shirley was a large house, but it was nearly always full of cousins and uncles and aunts, all come a-visiting, like Robert.

There was always a lot to do at Shirley. Robert went down to the stables the very first morning of his visit. There were so many horses in the stables he was sure that he could have one to ride.

"When I grow up," said Robert, "I shall have a horse of my own."

That seemed a long time to wait, but he could get ready while he was waiting. He was learning how to ride now, and how to take care of a horse.

His uncle was down at the stables.

"May I ride the gray horse?" asked Robert.

His uncle knew he could trust him. Robert would not ride the horse too hard. He would take good care of it.

The gray horse was brought out.

"I am riding over to the next plantation," said his uncle. "Would you like to go with me?"

Robert would. He watched his uncle make sure that his horse's blanket was folded the right way. He made sure the gray horse's blanket was just right, too. He sat straight in his saddle, just as his uncle sat. He was learning just how he should do when he had that horse of his own.

He did not know that, years afterward, when he had become General Lee, he would have over twenty thousand horses to care for. He knew, though, that he loved horses, and he knew that horseback riding was fun, indeed.

Away they went across the fields. The dogs ran after them. Oh, but it was a fine morning!

## 2. *Grandfather Carter*

Horseback riding, though, is hard exercise. Robert was glad to rest a little while that afternoon. He stretched out on a big rug in the hall.

Aunt Randolph was sitting by the fireplace. She was telling the smaller children a story.

Robert felt he was growing too big to ask for stories, but he liked to hear them, just the same. He wanted to listen to this one Aunt Randolph was telling.

"Away they went

across the fields."

"Your Grandfather Carter," said Aunt Randolph, "was a very rich man. He owned miles and miles of land. He owned many houses. He owned many slaves. When he went driving, he had six horses to draw his coach."

"Not many boys have a grandfather like that," thought Robert to himself. It made him feel very proud and lucky.

"But your Grandfather Carter always said," Aunt Randolph went on, "that those who have, must share.

"When the corn crop was poor on the James River, he brought great wagon loads of corn from some of his other farms, to help the neighbors who had none.

"When he sent a shipload of tobacco to England, to be sold, he always sent word that part of the money must be used to help the hungry people of London.

"Everyone always loved your Grandfather

Carter because he always shared with others."

Aunt Randolph stopped for a moment, and looked at them. "All of you are Carter grand children. Are you going to be like your grandfather?"

"I am," thought Robert. "I shall always share."

And he always did.

### 3. *Aunt Randolph's School*

That night, after supper, the children began to play in the hall. The younger children were playing one game, and the older children were playing another. They kept getting in each other's way. The older ones scolded. The younger ones were cross.

"Let's all play the same game," said Robert.

"What game?" they asked.

Robert thought quickly. The game must not

be too hard for the little children, but it must be fun for the big children, too.

"Let's play Blind Man's Buff," said Robert.

He tied a handkerchief over the eyes of the oldest girl. Soon he had them all playing.

It was a noisy game, but they were all playing together, and they were all having a good time. Nobody scolded, and nobody was cross.

Mother and Aunt Randolph sat by the fire-place watching. They did not mind the noise.

"You like to play with your cousins, don't you?" Aunt Randolph said to Robert.

"Yes, indeed," said Robert.

"You ought to send him to school at my house," Aunt Randolph said to Mother. "Then he could be with his cousins all the time."

"Maybe I shall," said Mother.

Robert knew about Aunt Randolph's school. Grandfather Carter had twenty-three children. Most of them were married now, and had children of their own.   No wonder Robert thought he had a few cousins!

There were so many Carter grandchildren that their parents had started two schools for them. There was a school for the Carter granddaughters at Shirley.   There was a school for the Carter grandsons at Aunt Randolph's.

Robert thought he would like to go to school there.   He was certainly glad he was a Carter grandson.

# XVI

## GOING TO THE FIRE

AS SOON as they came home from Shirley, Mother began to get Robert ready to go to Aunt Randolph's school. She and Ann sewed all day long.

They made him some white shirts with stiff, white ruffles. They made him some long yellow trousers, that were gathered in close at the ankle. They made him a jacket which was very tight and short. They knew that all the boys at Aunt Randolph's would have shirts and trousers and jackets just like these. They packed them all in a small leather trunk.

Robert was very busy, too. He and Spec had to go fishing one more time. They had to race once more over King George's meadows, where Spec could chase rabbits through the tall grass.

One afternoon, on their way home, they met Cousin Cassius.

"Look, Cassius," said Robert. "Spec knows a new trick. He——"

"Dong! Dong! Dong!" The sound of a great bell broke right into the middle of his sentence.

Robert did not wait to finish the trick. He and Cassius began to run. Spec ran after them. They all knew what that bell meant. It was calling as plainly as could be, "Fire! Fire!"

Soon the street was full of men and boys, all running in the same direction. Robert could see the smoke now. It was coming in great clouds from the windows of a house away down the street.

But the men didn't run down the street. Not yet. They ran the other way. They must get the fire engine first.

"Dong-dong! Dong-dong!" went the bell.

"Now they were at

the burning house."

You could almost hear it call, "Hurry! Hurry!"

The first person to see the fire had run to the store on the corner. He had got the key to the fire-engine house. He had rushed inside and had begun to ring the bell.

"Dong! Dong! Dong!"

"Look!" cried Robert. "Here it comes!"

A group of men had thrown the big doors open wide. They had taken hold of the long pole in front of the fire engine. They were pulling it across the wooden floor, out into the street.

Other men came running up. Soon there were over twenty of them pulling the big red engine. How it rattled over the rough cobblestones!

Now they were at the burning house. They stopped by the nearest well. The fire engine had a long hose. They dropped one end down into the well.

At each end of the fire engine were two long handles. One handle was close to the ground.

The other was up so high the men had to stand on the engine to reach it. Ten men could stand by each of those on the ground. Five men climbed up on each side of the engine. Then they began to pump. Up! Down! Up! Down! It was like working a great big see-saw.

They pumped water up from the well. It ran through the engine. Then it came through another hose, so hard and so fast that it reached the upstairs windows of the burning house.

"Hurray!" cried the crowd. "Hurrah!"

At last the fire was out. The men rolled up the hose. They pulled the fire engine back up the street.

Robert felt very sorry, though, for the people who lived in the burned house. The fire had burned up most of their furniture. The water and smoke had ruined the rest.

Robert thought of his own home, with its big table, its fine chairs, and its comfortable beds.

And, right away, he remembered Grandfather Carter.  Those who have, must share.

He hurried home to tell Mother about the fire. As soon as she heard about it, she said, "We must see what we can do for those poor people."

She fixed up a big bundle of things for them. Robert helped her fix it.

Of course, they were not rich as Grandfather Carter had been.  They could not bring whole wagon loads of corn to help their neighbors. They were glad, though, to do what they could to help.  They knew that Grandfather Carter was right.  Those who have, must share.

# XVII

## COMING HOME FROM SCHOOL

ROBERT stayed at Aunt Randolph's school until he was twelve years old. Of course, he wasn't there all the time. He came home every summer. He came home for Christmas, and for other holidays, too. But at last he came home for good.

A great deal had happened while he was away. When he was eleven years old, there had come a letter from Father. He was on his way home.

It made all of them very happy. Father had been away, you remember, ever since Robert was a little boy. Mildred didn't even remember him at all. Everybody was excited, as they made things ready for him.

But Father did not come. Instead, they received a letter. He had died on the way back.

There were no trains then. There were no fast boats. Father had died in the spring. It was fall before the letter reached them.

Father had said the children must take care of Mother. But Carter was away at college. And Ann was away up North. She had not been well for a long time. Mother thought that perhaps the doctors up North could help her. She went to stay with some friends there.

Now it was time for Smith to leave home. He was growing up, too. He was going into the Navy.

Mildred would be left alone with Mother. Mildred was just a little girl. Robert knew Mother needed *him*. He must keep his promise to Father. So Robert was going home.

It is a fine thing to feel that you are needed. And it is a very fine thing to be going home.

Robert was very, very happy when Nat came for him.

"How is Mother?" was the first question he asked.

The old negro shook his head. "Your Ma ain't so well," he said. "It 'pears like it hurts her even to walk across the room."

"She won't have to walk when I get home,"

" 'How is Mother?' "

said Robert. "I can carry her." He could hardly wait to start helping.

At last they were on their way. It was a fine trip. Sometimes, the road led through the woods. The sun shone down through the thick green leaves. There were brooks and mossy places, where the ferns grew thick.

The road ran uphill and downhill, and always it ran nearer home. "Tomorrow I shall go swimming with Smith," thought Robert. "What fun we'll have!"

Sometimes the road led past big fields of corn. Robert knew there were watermelon patches hidden in the cornfields. The watermelons were getting ripe. It made him thirsty just to think of them.

The road ran downhill and uphill, and always it ran nearer home. "I shall go to the Academy soon," thought Robert. "I am old enough now to study algebra, and Greek, and Latin, too."

Honeysuckle grew on the side of the road. Its leaves and flowers were covered with dust. The air was heavy with its sweet odor.

Now he could see, far away, the new steeple of Christ Church. He could see the houses of Alexandria. They were so far away, that they looked like tiny doll houses.

The road ran uphill and downhill, and always it ran nearer home. "I wonder what I shall do when I grow up," thought Robert.

The sun went down, and twilight came. Lightning bugs flew around the carriage, with their yellow lanterns. Down in the marshy places near the creek, the frogs were calling, "Cher-ump! Cher-ump!"

And now Robert had no time to think of anything more. They were rattling over the cobblestones of Washington Street. An old man was going slowly down the street. He was lighting the oil lamps on the big posts at each corner.

Nat stopped the horses in front of a small brick house.  Robert almost tumbled out of the carriage.  He ran up the stone stairs.

"Mother!" called Robert.  "Mother!"

He was home at last.

# XVIII

## A BUSY DAY

### 1. *Morning*

"BUR-DEE, bur-dee, bur-dee!" sang a red bird outside Robert's window. "Get-up, get-up, get-up!"

But Robert was already up. This fine spring weather was no time for sleepy heads.

First he must go to market. When he was a little boy, it had seemed a long way. Now he could get there and back "in a little less than no time."

He did not mind carrying the big market basket. He laughed because it made him think of a joke he had just heard. He must tell the joke to Mother. It would make her laugh, too.

The joke was about Justice John Marshall.

Justice Marshall was one of the most famous men in the United States. He did not look famous, though. He was tall and lean, and he liked to wear old clothes.

His wife was an invalid like Mother. Justice Marshall would go to market for her, in Richmond, just as Robert was going for Mother in Alexandria.

One day there was a young man in the Richmond market who had just bought a big turkey. The young man was dressed in fine clothes. He was too proud of himself to be seen carrying a turkey through the streets.

He saw a countryman in old clothes standing on the corner.

"Here," he told the old man, "come carry this turkey home for me. I'll pay you for doing it."

The old man took the turkey. He followed the young fellow home. Everyone who saw them laughed. The young man couldn't think why.

The old man carried the turkey to the kitchen door. Then he bowed to the young man.

"I wish you good day, sir," he said, and went off down the street.

"Who is that old fellow?" the young man asked his neighbor.

"Why, that is John Marshall, the Chief Justice of the Supreme Court of the United States."

How Mother would enjoy that joke! Robert was still laughing, himself, as he finished his marketing and hurried home.

Back home, breakfast was waiting for him. There was spoonbread, made of cornmeal and eggs and creamy buttermilk. He put plenty of butter on it, while it was still hot. My, but it was good!

After breakfast, he went back to his room for the key basket. Boys today like to carry keys in their pockets. They would have a hard time carrying Robert's keys there. His keys were big and clumsy. Some of them were six inches long. His pockets weren't big enough to hold them. He had to carry them in a basket.

He opened the pantry with them, and the store-

"He opened the pantry."

rooms.   He gave the servants the flour and eggs and everything else they would need during the day.   While his mother was sick, he not only had to go to market—he had to keep house, too.

Now it was almost school time. Robert peeped into his mother's room to see if she had awakened. The blinds were down to keep out the sun, but she saw him and smiled good morning.

Back in his own room, he packed up his school books.   There were Greek and Latin books now, and an algebra, to be carried with his slate.   He had started school at the Academy.   He must carry his slate very carefully so that he wouldn't rub off the sums he had worked on it last night.

Other boys with their books and slates met him on the way to school.

"What are you doing this afternoon?" they called to him.   "Let's go fishing down by Hunting Creek."

"Not this afternoon," said Robert.   "If the

weather keeps warm and the sun stays out, I have something else to do."

## 2. *Afternoon*

The weather kept warm and the sun stayed out. As soon as school was over, Robert hurried home.

"Come, Mother," he called. "You must go driving. The doctor said you must. Nat has already brought the carriage to the front door."

Mrs. Lee hardly ever went out, now. It hurt her even to walk across the room. But Robert had grown big and strong. He brought her her bonnet and shawl. Then he picked her up as if she were a doll-baby, and carried her out to the carriage.

He put her down very carefully. He piled cushions around her back. "Drive slowly," he told Nat. "We mustn't let her get jolted."

Nat drove very slowly. Mrs. Lee leaned back against the cushions. But Robert wasn't satisfied. She looked so tired and sad. The doctor said these drives wouldn't do her any good unless he could find some way to cheer her up. If only he could make her smile!

They drove down by the river, where the breeze was cold. Mother shivered a little.

"Goodness," said Robert. "This will never do! How can we keep that wind out?"

There was a newspaper in the carriage. Robert took out of his pocket the knife he used to mend his pens at school. He cut the newspaper in pieces. He pretended to make newspaper curtains to keep out the cold air.

He looked so very solemn about it that Mrs. Lee couldn't help smiling.

"That's fine!" said Robert.

Mrs. Lee laughed. Robert laughed, too. The drive was doing her good, already.

Tea was ready when they got home.  Mother ate more than she had for a long time.

### 3.  *Evening*

After tea, Robert brought his books to his mother's room, so that he could be with her while he studied.

"Squeak, squeak," went his pencil over the slate.

"Tick-tock," went the clock in the corner.

"Click, click," went Mother's knitting needles.

At last Robert put down his pencil.

"That is done," he told his mother.

"And it is just about bedtime," said Mother.

The clock said so, too.  And so did Robert's eyes.  He had been up since early morning.  He had worked hard all day.  Now he was sleepy as sleepy could be.

As soon as he had made Mother comfortable

for the night, he went to his own room. In a very, very short time he was in bed.

Far away, he could hear the night watchman. The watchman walked up and down the streets all night. He made sure that everything was safe. He would call out what time it was, too. Sometimes, he would tell you about the weather.

It was very comfortable to lie in bed, and listen to the watchman. First you could hear him away off. Then he came nearer and nearer.

"Ten o'clock and a clear sky!" called the watchman. Tomorrow would be another good day.

Now he had gone by. His voice sounded farther and farther away.

"Ten o'clock and a clear sky!"

But Robert didn't hear it at all. He was fast asleep.

# XIX

## ROBERT GOES HUNTING

WHEN fall vacation came, Robert went down to Stratford.

He wasn't a chubby little boy any longer. He was growing tall, and his back was straight as any soldier's. His hair was dark and wavy.

He liked to swim, and to hunt, and to ride. He was always joking, and full of fun.

He had been working hard all summer. Now he was ready for a good time. The girl cousin was visiting at Stratford again. She was ready for a good time, too.

They ran, together, through the big house from the square hall on the ground floor to the little walkways around the chimneys on the roof. They sang songs and played games the whole evening long.

The next morning, the girl cousin sat down by the fireplace to sew on her sampler. She was working the alphabet in cross-stitches while the boy watched interestedly.

"It looks like my old blue-backed speller," teased Robert. "A—b, ab."

"I'm going to embroider a whole verse of poetry after I finish the letters," the girl cousin told him. "And then I'll work a vine, with flowers, all around it."

"That will look very grand, indeed."

"I hope so, because it's supposed to be a sample of my sewing. That is why it's called a sampler. Wouldn't you like to stitch a sampler, Master Robert?"

"Indeed I wouldn't," said Robert. "That is a girl's work. But I'll bring you back a sample of my hunting. I'm starting for the woods right now."

First, though, he went out to the kitchen. He

got some cold chicken and biscuit to take with him for lunch.

When he started for the woods, George Washington Perkins ran after him.

"I'se coming, too, Marse Robert," he said. "I kin carry the bag."

"All right," said Robert.

The two boys went deeper and deeper into the woods. All day long they tramped under the great pine trees. The pine tags were soft under their feet. The wind whistled high over their heads.

When noon came, they rested for a while under a big tree. Wild grape vines hung down from the tree. George began to swing on the grape vines.

Robert took out his lunch. He gave the little negro half.

"Yonder is a persimmon tree," said George. "I wonder is any of the persimmons ripe yet."

"You'd better not taste them to find out," laughed Robert. "A green persimmon will just about turn your mouth inside out."

"No, suh," said George, "you don't catch me tasting green persimmons."

After they had rested a while, they went on.

Robert's father had wanted all of his boys to learn to shoot. Robert had practiced in the woods around Alexandria. He had gone hunting with Nat, until now he could shoot almost as well as a man. The bag began to grow very, very heavy.

"I reckon it's time us was starting for home," said the little negro.

"Just one more," Robert told him. "I want to have a full bag."

Clouds had come up over the sun. Suddenly, "plop!" a big rain drop hit Robert on the nose.

He looked up through the trees. The sky was dark.

"Maybe we *had* better hurry a little," he said. "You go on."

But the little negro stood still, with a frightened look on his face.

"Marse Robert," he said, "which way *is* home?"

Robert looked around. The woods certainly did look alike, whichever way he turned. Maybe he was frightened, too, but he didn't show it.

"We'll go this way," he said.

The rain began to come harder. The little negro shivered. "I'se skeered," he said.

"Now you don't need to be scared," Robert told him. "You know I'll take care of you."

"Yes, suh, Marse Robert. I knows."

They plunged through the wet woods. It had grown so dark they could hardly see in front of them. The pine tags were wet and slippery. Briars and vines caught at them and tripped them.

"We is lost," cried the little negro. "I just know we is lost."

But Robert kept on. He watched which side of the trees the moss was on. He watched which way the little brooks ran. He had what grown people called a "sense of direction."

"Here is the big tree where we ate our lunch," he said finally. "Don't you remember the grape vines?"

"Yes, suh. Now which way does we go?"

Robert thought hard for a minute.

"Let's see if we can find that persimmon tree, again."

It was almost dark now, but they hunted around until George called out, "Here 'tis."

"Fine! Now, this morning, when we came to this tree, the persimmon tree was on the left, so now, if we turn until it is on our right, we'll be facing towards home. See?"

They started off again. George was no longer

" 'Here 'tis!' "

afraid.  He knew "Marse Robert" would find
the way.

At last he cried out, "Yonder's the spring
house."

And sure enough it was.  They were safely
back home.

"I'm glad you got back," the girl cousin told
Robert that evening.  "Those woods are a terrible place to lose your way."

"Why I think," said Robert, "they're a fine
place to find your way.  And, as soon as the persimmons are ripe, George and I are going back
to get you a whole pailful."

## XX

### WHEN LAFAYETTE CAME TO TOWN

THE year that Robert was seventeen years
old, a very famous visitor came to the
United States from France. The Marquis de
Lafayette, when he was a very young man, had
come to America to help fight for freedom. Now,
when he was an old man, he was coming again.
He wanted to visit the country he had helped set
free.

He did not know how everybody in America
loved him. He wondered if, when he reached
New York, he could find a carriage to take him
to the hotel. To his surprise, he found thousands
of people waiting to cheer him. They had carriages decorated with ribbons. They marched
down the street in a big parade, shouting, "Hurrah for Lafayette!"

Everywhere he went, they had a big holiday. Schools and stores were closed. Flags decorated the street. "Hurrah for Lafayette!"

At last the news came that he would visit Alexandria. Robert was delighted. He longed for a chance to see this great hero who had done so much to help his country. So did everybody else.

You may be sure there was no school that day. The children must be able to tell their grandchildren, "Once upon a time, I saw Lafayette."

Across the street down which Lafayette would pass, they built a great arch. On it, in big letters, was written, "Welcome, Lafayette."

The sidewalks were crowded with men, and women, and children. They waved their flags and cheered. There were old men there who had fought in the same battles with Lafayette. There were young men who had heard their fathers talk about him.

Lafayette bowed and waved to them all as he passed.

Robert helped with the others to get ready for the big parade. He watched the carriage drive through the big arch.

"Hurrah for Lafayette!" he called.

Then, after it was all over, he hurried home to tell Mother about it. He thought it had been a very exciting day.

But the next morning was more exciting still. Soon after breakfast, a carriage drove up in front of his house. An old man got out. It was Lafayette himself!

Lafayette had known Father when he was a young man. They had been with Washington, together, during the war. He had heard that the wife of his old friend was still living in Alexandria. And, while all the city was cheering him, and having a holiday in his honor, Lafayette had come to call on Robert's mother.

He came up the front steps.   Nat opened the door for him.   Robert heard him ask for "Madame Lee."

After Mother had talked with him for a few moments, she sent for Robert.

" 'May I present my son, Robert?' "

"May I present my son, Robert?" she asked.

Lafayette said he was delighted to meet the son of his old friend. He told Robert and Mrs. Lee about his own children. But mostly he talked about Robert's father.

Robert never forgot that morning call. It was a crisp October day. Nat had built a fire in the big fireplace. The burning logs sputtered and sparkled.

In their warm light, Robert could see the face of the famous old gentleman who was Marquis de Lafayette. He could see the face of the dear little lady who was Mother. As the logs sparkled and sputtered, he listened to them talk about the brave gentleman who had been his father.

Of course, Mother was proud of her husband. How could she help but be? And Robert, watching them, made up his mind. Someday, she was going to be proud of her son, too.

# XXI

## FINISHING UP

ROBERT was working over his slate. With a ruler and a pencil, he was drawing his lines very, very carefully.

There had been many busy days in Mrs. Lee's home since Lafayette had called there. For Robert, too, had now decided to be a soldier. He was going to the Military Academy at West Point. Almost any day now, the orders would come for him to leave.

Mother was busy getting his clothes ready, and Robert was getting ready, too. The soldiers at West Point needed to know a great deal of mathematics. He was taking special mathematics lessons from the teacher who lived next door.

On the table close by were his father's own books. Robert's father, you remember, had been a soldier, too. Some of these books he had written himself, to show how General Greene had made his plans and moved his soldiers, to help win the Revolution.

They were very interesting books, and Robert knew it. He could almost feel them call to him, "Put down your slate and come read us."

But Robert kept on working. When he started a thing, he always liked to finish it. "Creak, creak," went his pencil over the slate.

Mother looked up from the shirts she was making.

"Haven't you worked long enough for to-day?"

Robert shook his head. "I want to finish this."

"But you told me quite a while ago that you had found the answer."

"I have. I'm copying it now, so it will be ready to hand in tomorrow. I want it to look just right." And Robert kept on working.

After a while there came a whistle under the window.

"Come on, Robert," called his cousin. "Let's go fishing once more before you leave for West Point."

"In a few minutes," Robert answered. "I want to finish this first."

His cousin came in to wait. He looked at Robert's slate.

"I wouldn't bother about being so careful," he said. "Just as soon as Mr. Hallowell looks at it tomorrow, you'll wash it off, you know."

"But that's no reason for not finishing it," said Robert.

He wrote down some more figures. He drew a last line very carefully. Then he looked over it, to make sure it was all right.

There were no smears on his slate. There were no ugly smudges. The work was as neatly and carefully done as if it were going to be printed in a book.

Robert put down his ruler. He put down his pencil.

"There," he said. "That's finished. Now let's go fishing."

" 'There! That's finished.' "

# XXII

## LEAVING HOME

### 1.  *Off for West Point*

ROBERT was leaving home.  His trunk was packed.  The horses and carriage were in front of the house.  Nat was holding the reins, waiting.

He would drive Robert down the road to the river.  He would take him across the Long Bridge to Washington.

Then Nat would drive back alone, and Robert would be on his way to West Point.

It was hard to say good-bye to Mother.  It was hard to say good-bye to the home where he had had so many good times.  Someday he would come back, but he wouldn't be a boy then.  He would be a man.

He thought of his mother and all she had done for him. He thought of his father, and his grandfather, and of all those other Lees who had helped to make Virginia history.

He knew that more could be expected of him than of most boys, just because he had had such a home, and such a family. It was not enough just to be proud of them. It was not enough just to love them. He must be brave as they had been brave. He must live as they would want him to live.

He must remember that he, too, was a Lee of Virginia.

"You'd better be starting, Marse Robert," called Nat. "It's getting late."

"I'm coming," said Robert.

He ran down the steps. He climbed into the carriage. Nat started the horses. Mother watched and waved until, finally, they were out of sight.

General Robert E. Lee of Virginia

## 2.    *General Robert E. Lee*

Someday you will read, in history, the rest of the life of Robert E. Lee.  You will read how he became a great soldier.

You will read how he built forts, and made rivers flow into new beds.

You will read how he fought through the Mexican War.

You will read how, when the sad war came that tore our country in two, he left the United States Army to stay with his own loved state of Virginia.

You will read how he fought bravely in the terrible years that followed—and lost.

And, finally, you will read how, after the war was over, he was greater and braver than he had ever been before.  You will read how he taught the thousands of people who loved him to forget war and hatred, and to live again in peace with their neighbors.

That is why, throughout all our country today, North, South, East, and West, we admire and love General Robert E. Lee, of Virginia.